WAJID & THE PERFECT PEARL

Tales from Old Araby

WAJID & THE PERFECT PEARL

Tales from Old Araby

CHRISTINE OSBORNE

OTHER WORKS BY THE AUTHOR

The Gulf States and Oman, Croom Helm, 1977
An Insight & Guide to Jordan, Longman, 1980
An Insight & Guide to Pakistan, Longman, 1981
Cooking the Middle Eastern Way, Prion, 1984
People at Work in the Middle East, Batsford, 1984
Middle Eastern Food and Drink, Wayland, 1988
Independent Travellers Guide to Morocco, Collins, 1990
Travels with My Hat: A Lifetime on the Road, 2013
Among Believers: A Pictorial Journey, 2016
The Gulf States and Oman: Routledge Library Editions,
History of the Middle East, Routledge, 2017
Old Gulf Coast Days: Qatar, 2018
Old Gulf Coast Days: United Arab Emirates, 2022
Old Gulf Coast Days: Sultanate of Oman, 2022

osbchristine@gmail.com
www.paperhorsedesign.com.au

ISBN 978-0-9923240-7-0 (pbk)

Front cover: Quiet scene in al-Ruwais, north coast of Qatar, 1975

CONTENTS

Introduction

INTRODUCTION

The discovery of vast oilfields in the mid-twentieth century bestowed all the riches of Aladdin's cave on the eastern states of the Arabian Peninsula. Nowhere else in the Middle East has oil wealth made such an impact on local society and traditional culture. In less than a generation, high-rise cities rose along the flat coastline of what is historically known as the Persian Gulf and many local traders and fishermen became millionaires almost overnight.

But the most remarkable rags to riches story surrounds the Bedouin, desert dwellers living in the arid hinterland. Generous resettlement schemes enabled the itinerant herders to exchange their nomadic existence for a sedentary lifestyle in new satellite villages built by the emirs, or rulers. In consequence, the epithet "nomad" has become obsolete in the Arab States of the Gulf, although Bedouin tribes are still found on the fringes of the great Empty Quarter in Saudi Arabia and Oman.

I was astonished by the economic development and social transformation in Dubai when I stopped there en route to Australia from London in 1974. The last of the big Kuwaiti *boums* were moored on Dubai Creek and, in what has since become the central business district, was a final sand patch where visiting Bedouin once hobbled their camels.

Fascinated by this ultimate glimpse of "Old Araby" I resolved to return and write a book on the region. A year later, a young Arab met in the UAE capital Abu Dhabi, neatly summarised the situation: he had swapped his camel for a Maserati and his entire family had packed up their goat-hair tents and were living in a seaside villa with chandeliers.

Invited for *qahwa* (Arabic coffee) with his mother, I asked if she missed anything of her old desert life. "I am so happy that instead of pulling up buckets of well water, I can now turn on a tap," her son translated for me. But her husband, a wrinkled old sheikh from the Liwa oasis, had not made a garden: he liked to feel the sand between his toes was the explanation.

For modern Arab youth, the peripatetic lifestyle of their forefathers is inconceivable, but while the traditional tents may have vanished, the camel remains an iconic symbol of the region's heritage.

The imagined characters in *Wajid & the Perfect Pearl* are based on research and memories of people I encountered while writing *The Gulf States and Oman*, almost fifty years ago. Considered a definitive account of the impact of oil on local society, it was republished in 2017 by Routledge Library Editions: *History of the Middle East.*

WAJID
& THE
PERFECT
PEARL

WAJID & THE PERFECT PEARL

The pearl diving season was the most important time of the year on the island when hundreds of men left their homes to work on the pearl boats.

Each *nakhuda*, or captain, gave his crew some money for their families during their absence. The captain of Omar's boat had advanced him more than could ever be repaid. This meant he was obliged to work on the same boat his entire life.

When the fleet was assembled, everyone came down to see it off. The men beat drums and sang sea shanties, but the women wept because they would not see their husbands and sons for as long as three months at a time.

The journey to the pearl reefs took two days sailing. When the boats arrived, they dropped anchor and at dawn the divers began work.

Every year since boyhood, Omar's eldest son Wajid had accompanied his father. A strong lad, his job was to lower his father down on a rope, weighted with a lump of rock.

Omar could remain underwater for up to two minutes while quickly cutting off shells. On rising for air, Wajid emptied his basket and the crew began opening the oysters. If a pearl was found, it was handed to the captain who dropped it in a small red bag.

On this journey to the pearl beds, Wajid noticed that his father was coughing.

The captain also noticed.

"Next season, Wajid, you must take your father's place as a diver," he said.

And Wajid could not disobey because his father was in the captain's debt.

When the fleet returned to the island, everyone was there to welcome them home. Now the women were laughing. And among the crowd were Fatima, Wajid's mother, and his two brothers, Ali and Mustapha.

The family house was located in the old part of town. It had three rooms: a kitchen that doubled for cooking and bathing, a room where the parents slept and another shared by the three boys.

Nearby was the big house owned by the merchant who bought and sold the pearls. It had twenty rooms with carved teak windows and a garden with date palms.

Omar continued to cough all that winter. Clearly, he could not dive again and Wajid accepted he would have to replace his father on the boat.

As the pearling season drew near, Wajid thought of the oysters anchored on the sea floor.

Island myth believed that pearls are made when the oysters come up to the surface and swallow drops of rain. A nice story, but it is untrue.

A pearl is formed when grit gets into the shell. The oyster does not like this and it builds up layers of shell around the irritant. After many years, this becomes a pearl: white, pink, yellow or grey.

Most pearls are small, like the seeds of a plant and are thus known as 'seed pearls'. Bigger ones are usually round and smooth. A big, round smooth pearl with no blemishes is known as a *dannah*, or a perfect pearl.

Wajid imagined discovering a *dannah*. He could see it waiting for him on the seabed. After all, Wajid in Arabic means: '*He who finds whatever he wants at the time he wants it.*'

He dreamed of a perfect pearl, valuable enough to repay their debt. He would buy his father a small shop to sell the spices Fatima used to flavour their meals. For himself, Wajid imagined having a black motorbike like the one ridden by the pearl merchant's son.

The following season seventeen-year-old Wajid sailed as a diver and this time his father acted as puller.

Like the other divers, he wore a nose clip and rubber tips on his fingers to protect against the sharp-edged oysters. Slinging the basket around his neck, he stood on the stone which Omar lowered carefully into the sea.

On reaching the pearl beds, Wajid let go the rope and began swimming about cutting off shells with a small knife and collecting them in his basket. After several dives, his confidence grew. On one day, he made more than fifteen descents.

After ten days diving, Wajid's boat anchored over a reef where every diver brought up an oyster-shell containing a pearl.

"If a 'perfect pearl' exists, it must be here," thought Wajid.

That night a terrible storm blew up. When dawn broke, three of the pearl boats were missing, believed to have sunk, and so the other captains decided to return early.

It was a tragic homecoming, but wasting no time, Wajid visited an old Indian fisherman who lived by the dhow harbour.

"Lend me your boat," he told him. "I cannot promise anything, but trust in Allah and I will pay you back."

Returning home, he told his father and brothers of his plan to find the 'perfect pearl'.

"I know where it is, but we must hurry, the diving season is almost over," he said.

Next morning, they carried fruit, water and blankets down to the boat. The Indian had left them a knife, a basket and coral-stone anchor on the deck. He had also left a bill for twenty dinars.

"We will either be richer, or poorer than ever," laughed Omar. And raising the sail, they set off.

With a stiff breeze blowing, the small *sambuq* reached the pearl beds in three days when Wajid began searching for signs of the reefs. The first clue would be a freshwater spring bubbling in the sea. Another was a big pink coral head shaped like a potato.

The water was colder and darker than on the last occasion with the pearling fleet.

"I must hurry," thought Wajid. "The bad weather will return soon."

He swam about looking for the coral head, watched by a school of small silver fish and a big red rock cod.

Finally, on the third day of diving, Wajid came upon the elusive coral head around which were clusters of oysters.

On the following dive when he brought up the basket, his brothers were shouting and cheering.

"You are finding pearls!" they cried.

"Are they big pearls?" asked Wajid, hanging onto the side of the boat.

"Oh son," said his father who was opening oysters, "I have never seen a *dannah* in thirty years of diving."

Wajid began diving ever deeper. At twelve metres, his head felt dizzy.

"I must find the pearl," he gritted his teeth.

Cutting off the last oysters, he tugged on the rope to go up. Slowly he rose until breaking the surface he gasped for air.

"*Mashallah,*" cried Omar. "You have found the perfect pearl!"

The words filled Wajid's ears as he climbed on board. In his father's hand lay a gleaming cream pearl the size of a grape. And it was perfectly round.

"Show us!" cried Ali and Mustapha, but jumping up in order to see, they knocked their father's hand and the precious pearl fell on the deck and rolled into the sea.

For a long time no one spoke. Finally it was Omar himself who said: "Do not cry boys. We were not born to be rich. Be happy that you have at least seen a *dannah*."

Wajid sadly counted out the seed pearls. There were sufficient to pay for the loan of the boat, but not enough to free him from a lifetime of diving.

"Our journey must not be in vain," he said philosophically. "The Indian's nets are in that box. Let's catch some fish to take home to mother."

The four of them cast the net which sank out of sight. "Pull together," instructed Wajid and as they pulled the net came up and in it was the big red rock cod.

"Only one fish, but a big fish," said Mustapha.

Just then the cod opened its mouth and spat out a pearl.

It was the *dannah*!

"He has brought the pearl back to us. We must spare his life," cried Wajid. And picking up the slippery fish by its tail, he dropped it overboard.

It was early evening when they reached the island to find both Fatima and the Indian waiting on the wharf.

"Oh!" said the Indian, "Such a big pearl. It will certainly pay for the loan of my boat".

"It will pay for your boat, repay the captain's loan and we will still be rich!" laughed Wajid.

"I will buy a sewing machine," said his mother.

"I will buy a football," said Ali.

"I will buy a model plane," said Mustapha.

"And if anything is left after father has his shop, I will buy a motorbike," cried Wajid doing a little dance.

The next day, Wajid took the pearl to the merchant's shop where he sat sorting seed pearls. Shown the *dannah*, the merchant held it up to a lamp.

"A good pearl," he laughed. "I will give you 500 *dinar* for it."

"That is not enough for a perfect pearl," said Wajid.

"Yours is a poor family. 500 *dinar* is more than enough," the pearl merchant responded.

"Then I will keep it, rather than sell it for this sum," said Wajid, taking the pearl back.

On reaching home, he was surprised to find a man in a long white robe talking with his father.

"Peace be upon you," the visitor spoke gently to Wajid.

"I'm sorry we only have a mat to sit on," Wajid replied.

"Never mind," said the man. "You may be poor tonight, but you will be well off tomorrow for I have offered your father 3000 *dinar* for the *dannah*.

Wajid listened curiously as the man explained the reason for this unexpected visit.

"I have travelled to your island from the far away Kingdom of al-Mutakabbir," he said in his soft voice. "I have been sent by the king to find the perfect pearl for his sword."

And he opened a long wooden box in which lay a gleaming steel sword. Its hilt was lavishly decorated with precious red and green gems, except for an empty space in the centre.

Taking the pearl, Wajid dropped it delicately into the hole.

It was a perfect fit.

"Excellent! What better place for the perfect pearl than the king's sword?" said the man, and he began counting out the money…

~~~

A CAT
CALLED
AZIZ

A Cat Called Aziz

A tourist on seeing the cat sitting outside the incense shop, called him Frank. After frankincense. But the cat took no notice. Having sat on the steps of the shop for ten years, Aziz (for this was his real name) was indifferent to comment.

Another jokester, Aziz thought he might have been British, suggested a good name for him was 'Mus-cat' after Muscat, the capital of Oman.

Aziz thought this a little pathetic since Muscat was located around the next bay. He lived in Muttrah the port area, fish market and *souq*, so the man had simply made himself look foolish.

Aziz bin Sultan al-Hamra, to use his full name, was a part-tortoiseshell cat of origins obscure. His very pointed ears lent credence to a suggestion of royal descent. Had his ancestors once padded delicately around the Queen of Sheba's palace?

Bin Sultan means son of Sultan, a shrewd operator whose base was the fish market. Sultan had lived to a great age, fed on sardines and tuna scraps from the Arabian Sea.

No one knew Aziz's mother, a mystery cat who had delivered three kittens behind the mosque. But there were very few cats in Oman so perhaps she had once been a feral cat whom Sultan had met on one of his nightly strolls.

On seeing the kittens, a Danish embassy wife had taken them home. But only Aziz, the first born, had survived. When the

Danes were posted to Moscow, their driver took the kitten to his brother who owned the incense shop in the *souq*.

And there the kitten had stayed. From an early age he took to sitting on the step watching passers-by. He never did anything beyond watch. It wasn't necessary. And as the only cat in the *souq* he was treated like royalty.

Old Mohammed who sold canes, ropes and sticks of tobacco brought him titbits from the butcher. Leila who lived in one of the tall, white waterfront houses put milk in a tin lid as she passed.

The man who owned the incense shop contributed nothing towards his welfare, but Aziz felt this was fair as he allowed him to sit on the step.

Rents were expensive in the *souq* which had more than a hundred shops lining its narrow lanes. If he had to pay for a space on the step—perish the idea, thought Aziz.

And why the incense shop? He could have sat outside the baker or the money changer.

But no. He liked the fragrance of smouldering resin, sandalwood and aloe, but especially the silvery beads of frankincense from Dhofar province in southern Oman.

He liked to sit on the step and inhale its scent, imagining himself in the Queen of Sheba's household. With slaves to brush his coat and trim his claws.

~~~

THE
BENEVOLENT
DATE
PALM

The Benevolent Date Palm

The oasis had long been an important halt for desert travellers. No one knew its age, but clay tablets record that date farming was practised in the fertile river valleys of ancient Mesopotamia, the region occupied by present-day Iraq, Syria and Turkey.

The hundred or so date palms in the oasis were sustained by an underground spring and in the centre of the circle stood a single palm, taller than all the others. For the incense caravans plodding north and for coastal traders headed south, it was a local landmark, since to lose one's way meant almost certain death.

The date palm species belongs to the *Arecaceae* family of flowering plants. The exceptizonally tall palm was owned by Mohammed al-Faludi of the Bani Yas tribe of Bedouin in eastern Arabia.

Mr al-Faludi lived with his wife Zeinab and family, teenagers Ali and Aisha and their younger brother Jaffar, on a rocky outcrop overlooking the oasis. Their house was so close that at night, before falling asleep, they could hear the palm fronds scratching together in the wind.

With little else of value, a man's wealth in this remote interior village was equated with the number of date palms he owned. This meant that Mr al-Faludi, who technically possessed only one palm, was not well off.

In fact, he had once owned three. One had been sold to buy a camel. The other was sacrificed to meet their needs, the felling of a palm being an almost sacred ritual, similar to cutting down a coconut palm in the Pacific Ocean.

Nothing was wasted when a date palm crashed to earth. Staked out in the sand, its branches made an enclosure for goats. Raked out and combed, its fibrous heart could be woven into mats, baskets and brooms while the wood chips were gathered for use as fuel.

But while poor in one sense, Mr al-Faludi was rich in another—for Ar-Rahman "the Beneficent" (as the family called the palm) produced more dates than two or three other palms combined.

The year Aisha turned eighteen, it yielded a massive 250 pounds of soft golden fruit the sale of which was enough to keep them in food for a year.

However not only did Ar-Rahman produce the most dates in the oasis, the palm was the social heart of the village community.

In the early morning schoolchildren assembled beneath its shady canopy to learn the Qur'an in which are found many references to dates. Verse 19:25 *"And shake towards thyself the trunk of the Palm Tree: it will let fall fresh ripe dates upon thee."*

With the sun at its zenith, women, among them Zeinab, spread out mats beneath the palm to picnic on dates and *khubz* unleavened bread. Some would take out their basket weaving or make ropes from twisted date palm fibre. Others, tired from housework, simply lay down for a nap.

Late afternoon saw the male villagers take up places under the palm. All discussions and collective decisions were taken there—issues such as water rights and the current price of dates. Marriages were also arranged.

In the evening cool, the old folk arrived for an hour of story-telling. Of the time a sheikh from the coastal capital had bought the entire harvest for *iftar* break-fast during Ramadan.

"Dates are the fertilisers of our knees. They give us strength and energy," said 70-year-old Mr al-Faludi. The problem being that he was no longer young.

He had married late and his eldest child Ali would normally be expected to take over maintenance of the palm—performing chores such as thinning its branches, covering the bunches of fruit as protection from birds and clearing any nests.

Sadly, however, Ali had sprained an ankle so scaling the trunk to harvest this year's crop of dates was out of the question.

Jaffar was only twelve, so that left Aisha, a lively girl who loved riding the camel and who always helped Zeinab carry their water jars home from the spring.

"Women do not climb date palms in our society," her father told her firmly, but kindly, over the evening meal.

But date sales provided their only income so what was the family's alternative?

Early next morning Aisha took their saw and, winding a rope around her waist, she began slowly climbing the palm, carefully placing her feet in grooves on the trunk as she'd watched Ali do.

Reaching the crown, she began sawing off the stems allowing the bunches of fruit to fall to the ground.

"*Mashallah!* Well done!" Ali called up to her.

With the date merchants expected to arrive either that day or the next, the siblings had managed to harvest the date crop just in time.

But Mr al-Faludi was aghast.

"What will the community say of a girl climbing palms?" he cried.

"Nothing. They must accept it," said Zeinab coming to her daughter's defence. "It is time that women play a greater role other than cooking and sweeping sand from the house."

Ali laughed.

"Aisha will fetch a good bride price. She can do all the housework and also climb date palms as well as any man!"

~~~

THE
WHITE
FALCON

THE WHITE FALCON

The falcon glided effortlessly in the hot air pockets rising off the desert. He had not eaten and his sharp eyes swept the dunes for a sign of life. Two years old, he displayed the strong claws and the thin, tapered wings of the *Falconinae* sub-family of raptors. The difference was he was white.

Suddenly he spotted a movement in the sand. Hovering overhead, he plummeted some twenty metres then dropped like a stone.

Facing into the wind as falcons do when eating, he was unaware a decoy pigeon was being pulled towards a bush. Suddenly a net flashed out and he was trapped.

"Alhamdulillah!" exclaimed the Bedouin who'd tracked the bird for days.

The sport of falconry, where wild birds are caught and trained to hunt, is known to have been practised in the Middle East as long ago as 3500 BCE. It is mentioned in the Sumerian poem, *The Epic of Gilgamesh*, and remains just as popular with present-day sheikhs.

For the Bedouin in Arab society, falconry was not so much a sport as a vital means of obtaining food in a harsh desert environment.

The emphasis in training a captured bird is to harness its natural hunting ability in partnership with its owner. Falconry could also become a means of lifting a family out of poverty since a well-trained raptor can be worth a lot of money.

Donning a leather glove against its claws, Fuad (for that was the man's name) slipped a hood over the bird's head and walked back to his tent where his son, Hussain, had been waiting.

"What a beautiful bird!" whistled the boy.

The falcon could not see, but opening his wings to fly, he was stopped by the leather straps they had slipped on his legs. Eventually he calmed down and sat quietly on a perch they had stuck in the sand.

"Don't be afraid bird," said Hussain, gently stroking the falcon's back. "I will take care of you. But you must learn to hunt with me."

The falcon was not fed that day. The following morning the hood was removed and he sat blinking in the sunlight. He saw Fuad brewing coffee on a charcoal fire. And he saw Hussain holding out a piece of meat which he grabbed hungrily.

On with the hood, off with the hood… each day the lesson was repeated.

Finally, after weeks of training, Fuad decided it was time to introduce the bird to strangers. He put on his sports jacket, worn on visits to the village, and they set off on foot through the dunes.

It was market day with many falcons on display, but all eyes were on the white falcon sitting on Fuad's gloved hand.

"It's the first white falcon I have ever seen," said the spice merchant, himself a keen falconer.

"A gift from Allah," murmured the Imam of the Friday Mosque.

"Are you going to sell it?" the money changer smiled as he sighted Fuad and Hussain. Suddenly Hussain felt sad that the falcon might be sold, but he said nothing to his father and they returned to their tent.

The following day Hussain resumed teaching the bird to obey. Standing a hundred feet away from its perch, he swung a pigeon wing on a rope around his head, a traditional training method.

Some raptors can fly at speeds of 200 mph and the white falcon was no different. Each time Hussain swung the wing, the bird struck it like a bolt of lightning to be rewarded with a morsel to eat.

Then came the moment when Fuad removed his straps, but the falcon did not fly off as he had become accustomed to Hussain as his food source.

"Excellent, he will bring a good price," said Fuad and they set off once again for the village.

"Now is our chance," said Fuad to Hussain as the money changer approached them.

"So, you have come to sell your bird," said the money changer, stretching out its wings.

"He will be a good hunter," said Fuad. "And no one else has a white falcon."

The deal was done quickly and Hussain sadly handed over the falcon to its new owner.

"A prize falcon!" the money changer told his wife. "Tomorrow I will test him against the spice merchant's bird."

Early next day they set off to a spot where the Bedouin had reported seeing bustard, a bird prized by Arab falconers for its delicate meat.

"*Houbara!*" shouted the money changer as a grey bird rose up from the dunes.

"*Yallah!*" cried the spice merchant throwing the brown falcon off his glove.

The men watched it strike the bustard, bringing it to the ground. But the bird was hopping: she had hurt her leg. It was the end of her hunting that day.

"Let's see your expensive bird in action," said the spice merchant defiantly.

When a second bustard was spotted, the white falcon flew off like a bullet and hit the heavier bird in an explosion of feathers.

"He is a splendid hunter," said the money changer proudly.

But the white falcon wanted to be free. It was the first time since his capture he could spread his wings. And instead of returning to the money changer, he flew off into the sky.

The next day, feeling miserable, Hussain got up later than usual. The falcon had not left his side and now it was gone. He slowly washed his face in a dish, took a handful of dates and went out to feed the goats.

"Ya salaam!" The beautiful bird was sitting on its perch.

"Father!" he shouted. "The falcon has returned!"

"I know," said Fuad. "It flew back this morning while you were still asleep."

"And the money changer has been. Whether white or not, he doesn't want a falcon that is not well trained. I had to return his money.

"Can we keep him then?" cried Hussain.

"Of course, son," Fuad smiled. "Money won't buy happiness and I don't want to see you with a glum face for the rest of my life."

≈≈≈

AHMED
THE
RED SEA
FISHERMAN

AHMED THE RED SEA FISHERMAN

Ahmed had never known such a terrible storm. He struggled with the wheel of the fishing boat as his crew clung onto the pitching vessel. Thunder rolled and lightning flashed and the rain pelted down so hard it stung their faces.

Floats and boxes of fish broke loose, crashing from one side of the boat to the other. Sent spinning across the deck, baskets of prawns smashed into the cabin, spilling their contents.

The men prayed for Allah's guidance on the journey back to shore. Even on a calm day the occasional dhow ripped open its hull on offshore reefs. But one of the oldest and most experienced sailors in Gudaibiya, Captain Ahmed bin Zayed al-Hassan, steered them safely home with all the knowledge of a blind man on his walk for the morning newspaper.

Gudaibiya was the largest of half a dozen small fishing villages scattered along the Red Sea coast of Saudi Arabia. It had an old coral-stone mosque, a covered fish market and three shops: a general store owned by an old Hindu trader, a teahouse and a chandler selling ropes and cables, canvas, paint, oil, fishing equipment and other marine items.

Last in a row of twenty buildings lining the waterfront, Ahmed's house accommodated two wives and four children in its three rooms. One room served for cooking, eating and entertaining. The other two were the family bedrooms.

When Ahmed was with one wife, the second wife shared a bed with the kids. During the fiery summer, the entire family slept outside on woven palm frond mats. The three youngest children attended the *madrassa* or Qur'anic school in the mosque.

Isa, the son of Ahmed's first wife helped on the boat that Ahmed called *al-Haidi* meaning 'the guide'. Three villagers acted

as crew making a total of five hands to fish, cook their meals and trim the 30-foot-long vessel powered by an ancient two-stroke inboard engine.

A typical fishing trip lasted two or three days during the cooler months. Or a maximum 24 hours in summer when, without ice, the fish quickly deteriorated in the heat.

Their basic equipment included handlines, a gaff and two Japanese-made nylon nets. Ahmed also owned two traditional wire fish traps or *gandours* which were dropped on the outward voyage and collected on return.

The night before a fishing trip everyone slept early and awakened at dawn for *al-Haidi* to slip out as the rising sun lit up the emerald channel through the reef.

By six o'clock, they would be well out to sea with the crew trailing bait lines. With Isa at the wheel, Ahmed proved himself an excellent fisherman as well as an expert navigator, catching three fish to the others' one apiece.

Musa was the strongest of the villagers who lead the pulling of the net. On most days, depending on the tide, the catch included

mackerel, mullet, halibut and the sardines that shoal in millions along the Red Sea coast.

At noon the men stretched out under a shady canopy while Musa prepared a simple meal of rice and fish grilled over a charcoal brazier in the stern. As captain, Ahmed served himself first, using his right hand to break off a piece of mullet and pop it in his mouth.

When everyone had eaten, the crew took turns to use a lavatory known as a 'thunder box' hanging off the stern. Each man then washed his face and hands in a small bowl before offering a prayer facing north, the direction of Mecca.

With the anchor raised, *al-Haidi* moved to a new fishing spot. Lines were baited and the men sat quietly alert in the gathering darkness.

Different and bigger fish attacked at night. A shark was welcome as fillets from even a 50 lb fish would feed their families (46 people in all) and the rest of the fish could be sold for a profit.

By dawn the hold was a quarter full and a shovelnose shark, landed by Ahmed, lay on the deck. On the return trip to Gudaibiya, the *gandours* were lifted and found to contain several crabs and a large pink octopus.

Unloaded onto the village wharf, the catch was carried into the market. Early morning shoppers got the best choice. The crabs sold quickly and latecomers shared the shark which was big enough to go all round.

A good haul of seafood meant Ahmed could pay his crew at once with the profit sustaining his family for a week. Like the other hard-working, but poor fishermen of Gudaibiya, the al-Hassans owned few possessions—although life improved during the month of the *hajj* pilgrimage.

At this time, Ahmed used *al-Haidi* to convey pilgrims up the coast to Jeddah, from where they continued overland to visit the holy cities of Mecca and Medina. There were never a great many pilgrims coming from this direction. Those who did come had to continue by boat as the road stopped after Gudaibiya.

With a good stern wind, the voyage took only two days. The most passengers Ahmed had ever carried was twenty-four pilgrims from Hodeidah in the Republic of Yemen, at the mouth of the Red Sea.

Ahmed always spent a night in Jeddah, but intimidated by the big city, he stayed in the port with other dhow captains from Egypt, Somalia and the Sudan.

The fare money was spent on clothes for his children and presents of kohl and perfume for his wives. It was also an opportunity to stock up on tinned foods which were half the price of the Hindu's store.

Jeddah was also his only true day off from the sea. If *al-Haidi* made port in the afternoon, he treated himself to the cinema. Not so much for the movie as to relish the air conditioning which, along with electricity, had not yet reached Gudaibiya…

KAZEM
THE
KNAFEH
KING

KAZEM THE KNAFEH KING

At six o'clock in the evening, Kazem sliced his hundredth portion of *knafeh*, a creamy cheese pastry known as the 'King of Sweetmeats' in the Middle East.

Thursday afternoons were always busy, but this day had been exceptional. Wiping his hands on his apron, he called out to his brothers to say he was going to the *hammam*.

He walked through the crowded bazaar, turning left at the coppersmith, right at the spice merchant and left again at the mosque next to which wisps of steam spiralled out of the dome of the public bath-house.

Kazem greeted several shopkeepers on his way in and stripping off his clothes in an ante room he handed them to an attendant in return for a towel.

Stretched out on a marble bench, he was soaped and pummelled until well-scrubbed, he stood up and made his way along a steamy passage to the heart of the *hammam*.

There he selected a stool and a plastic bucket, filling the bucket with warm water running from a tap in the wall. Sitting down beside other bathers, he vigorously washed off every last stubborn bit of pastry.

Then, wrapping the towel around his hips, he returned to the courtyard where other men sat waiting their turn. Some were engaged in conversation, others smoked *nargila* pipes whose gentle bubbling added to the relaxed atmosphere of the *hammam*.

Sighting Kazem, a boy brought him tea and a sweetmeat.

"La, shokran!" said Kazem. No thank you! He did not want to see another pastry until work began again on Saturday at 7am.

HHK al-ZAHIR PATISSERIES had occupied the same corner of the bazaar for fifty years. Kazem's father said it was his grandfather's idea, a migrant escaping persecution in Iran.

The shop was owned by Mr Hussein al-Zahir and his three sons: Hassan, Hosni and Kazem.

Al-Zahir senior had since retired, but his sons ran it with military precision. Hosni and Kazem made the pastries while Hassan served the customers.

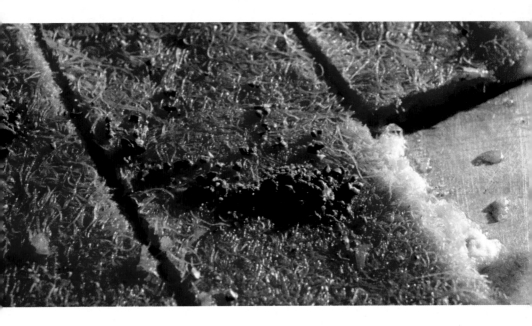

Middle Eastern peoples are historically fond of sweetmeats. On prominent religious days such as *eid ul-fitr* (at the end of the fast month of Ramadan) it is customary to take sweetmeats when visiting family members and friends.

Instead of the time-consuming procedure of cooking their own, many women prefer to buy sweetmeats freshly baked. A shop such as al-ZAHIR PATISSERIES was therefore a very good business. But as Kazem would point out, it was very hard work.

The middle brother, 24-year-old Kazem was responsible for making *knafeh*, a sweetmeat believed to have its origins in the Holy Land.

Working in the basement, he would fill a utensil like a large salt shaker with liquid batter and with great panache for anyone watching, he poured fine streams into a heated pan.

Instantly the strings crispened and he scraped them off into a greased tray. This was then topped with a sheet of soft, white cheese and another layer of vermicelli-like crispy strings, before being returned to the oven.

Once the top had browned, it was buttered, then inverted, before being cooked for a further fifteen minutes. Finally removed, the tray was allowed to cool before being drenched with syrup.

With his *knafeh* cooking, Kazem helped Hosni make the dozens of other pastries sold in the shop.

Baklava, a sticky honey and pistachio nut sweetmeat, was loved by all. In particular by the dentist who would buy a kilo a day, yet he still swore his teeth were his own.

Ma'amoul date cookies and *basbousa*, a yoghurt and syrup semolina cake, together with other popular choices, were arranged like works of art in the window display.

The town's new tourists could not pass the shop without stopping to look. Inevitably lured inside, but unsure what to choose, they were guided by Kazem to his tray of *knafeh*. On one memorable occasion, al-ZAHIR PATISSERIES counted twelve Germans seated at their laminate-top tables, all eating *knafeh*, baked just moments before.

By way of thanks, their guide was given a box of cashew-nut *halva* with the shop's name printed on the lid.

All three sons lived with their parents in a big house in the old Persian merchant's quarter by the creek. Built by grandfather al-Zahir, its roof featured iconic wind towers to capture any cooling breeze in the hot summer months. Eldest son Hassan, his wife and baby occupied one room, bachelors Kazem and Hosni shared a second while their parents lived on the ground floor whose courtyard contained a single orange tree.

Kazem was fond of Western pop music. On a Friday night, he and a few friends sometimes visited the discotheque in the town's first ever hotel. However, he rarely stayed up late as he did not drink alcohol and it was hard to meet local girls who sat shyly at a table by themselves.

One memorable Friday evening, Kazem met a Swedish girl employed by the hotel to set up a spa, the western equivalent of a *hammam*.

Tall and blonde, Freja spoke a little Arabic and although Kazem had never before danced with a woman, he invited her and smiling, she accepted.

Every night the following week Kazem practised his dance steps with Hosni: Abba's 'Dancing Queen' was a favourite at the time.

By the second Friday when he again met Freja, he danced quite well and Freja was quite smitten by the handsome young man.

On the third Friday Kazem invited Freja home for tea and sweetmeats, but while the al-Zahir parents were of course polite, they had always insisted their sons marry Muslim girls.

Kazem knew this meant marriage to his cousin Halima, but long after Freja had returned to Stockholm, he kept her photo above the *knafeh* oven until finally it turned brown with the heat.

~~~

THE OLD CARPET FINDS A HOME

The Old Carpet Finds a Home

The old carpet had been in the shop for so long that no one could remember when it had arrived. Many years ago it had been red and blue, but now its colours were hidden under layers of desert dust.

The carpet was the creation of two Bedouin women taking turns at a loom in their tent. When one of them was cooking, or putting the children to sleep, the other would sit down to weave, drawing the wool tightly across the loom, tying each knot precisely 300 times per square inch.

When the carpet was finished, it measured eight feet long by four feet wide and everyone who visited the tent declared it to be the most beautiful carpet they had ever seen.

The carpet's early life had been a happy one, but when it became old and dirty, the family decided to sell for a few *dirhams* to the carpet merchant in the *souq*.

Every evening since then, other traders had called in to exchange news but none of them bothered to look at the carpet on the floor. They walked on it, sat drinking coffee on it and alas, one or two men even ashed their cigarettes on it.

When any tourists came into the shop, the old carpet hoped they might show an interest, but they always bought the new rugs pinned on the walls. Even on a particularly busy week, when all the rugs were sold, still no one looked at the carpet beneath their feet.

By now the old carpet had been in the shop for so long it knew the price of everything else.

The copper trays, the pottery incense burners, the leather sandals, the amber beads—it even knew the cost of the spices arranged in baskets outside on the footpath. Yellow turmeric, red

paprika and tawny cumin sold for five, ten and fifteen *dirhams* per 100 grams.

During all this time the old carpet's only companion was a hubble-bubble pipe the rug merchant smoked with his friends.

The *nargila* liked to tell it stories of the famous sheikhs and generals who had smoked it.

"I am even older than you are," it sighed. "But I am now too old to care."

The difference between the carpet and the *nargila* was that the merchant took good care of the pipe. Each morning he brought it out and polished it and should someone wish to buy it, he would say it was not for sale.

Once when the *nargila* was not busy talking about itself, the old carpet whispered that it was really red and blue .

"Blue?" the pipe had hubbled and bubbled. "Why you're brown like the desert!"

Many more years were to pass before the day a foreign stranger walked into the shop.

"How much is that rug?" he said, touching the old carpet with his toe.

"What? That old thing? You can have it for $50," said the merchant, causing the old carpet to feel humiliated. Now I know I am nothing, it thought, since the new rugs cost fifty, even a hundred times more than this amount.

But a deal was struck and before the old carpet could say goodbye to the *nargila,* it was rolled up and taken back to the stranger's hotel.

Unrolling the carpet in his room, the man squatted down to count its knots which made the old carpet very frightened indeed. What if I am to be cut into prayer mats, it worried?

But the man had no intention of such a heinous act. A famous English carpet buyer, he took the old carpet with him back to

London and to a showroom filled with hundreds of rugs made in Central Asia, Turkey and Iran.

Given a steam bath, the old carpet slowly began to change colour from brown to red and blue just as it remembered.

"Antique Bedouin carpet £3000," said the shop owner, pinning a sign on the carpet and placing it in the window.

"Goodness," the old carpet said to no one in particular. "£3000 would buy the shop in the *souq*. Were the *nargila* here in London, it would not recognise me!"

And although many people visited the showroom, no one could afford such a price and the old carpet spent the winter alone in the window watching the snow falling, then melting, and finally the new buds growing on trees in the square.

Then one day a man wearing a long white robe stopped outside and, stroking his beard a moment, he came in and bought the old carpet paying £3000 in £100 notes taken from a plastic bag.

At first silent, the other carpets in the showroom suddenly all began talking at once.

"I remember that man," said a fine red and black Turkoman rug. "He came in last year and bought one of us for an Arab ruler."

Once again the old carpet was rolled up and put on a plane, but this time when it landed, it could hear familiar music and smell the coffee of home.

Driven to the emiri palace it was spread out in the *majlis* for everyone to admire. The cooks came in from the kitchens and the gardeners from the gardens. Even the women from the harem were permitted a glance.

"Such a magnificent carpet must not lie on the floor where people walk," declared the Sheikh striding in. Hang it in the mosque for everyone to see," he commanded.

And thus the old carpet found a home—in the *House of God*.

THE
BLACK
RIBBON
ROAD

THE BLACK RIBBON ROAD

Approaching the island, the dhow dropped its sail and glided towards the beach where Abdullah stood in a crowd of men. The dhow's arrival was an important event. Even the ruler himself had come to watch it unload.

Abdullah and his family lived on the mainland. Twice a year they travelled to the coast and crossed to the island to buy supplies. Like the other Bedouin, their needs were modest, but on this occasion, along with rice, salt, sugar and tea, Abdullah had wanted to buy a carpet.

Around five hundred people, mainly fishermen, lived on the island. Small, it was flat and treeless, but it had a well where Abdullah's camels had drunk after their five-day journey from the hinterland.

Rashid, the big brown camel, had carried his wife Moza and their tent. His sons Sultan and Sayed had shared the other male. Abdullah himself rode Jamila, a fine, fleet-footed female who provided them with milk.

Now the crew began unloading their cargo. Bags of cement, ladders, ropes, bundles of hay, plastic buckets and bolts of brightly coloured cloth were thrown down onto the sand.

Cartons marked FRAGILE RADIOS were handled carefully. The music they played excited the crowd, but Abdullah ignored it. He'd waited a week for the dhow and he was anxious to return home.

A meal taken in the desert was usually bread, rice and dates with meat only eaten on a special occasion such as a tribal wedding. Today, however, Abdullah had bought a fish which made a welcome change for supper.

Next morning, with the carpet packed behind him on Jamila, they moved off to where the camels crossed to the mainland at low tide.

Soon the island lay behind them and as they plodded further inland, Abdullah was surprised to see grass in the sands.

"It has rained!" exclaimed their cousin Bilal. "The first rain for four years."

"Allah be praised," Abdullah replied.

Rain foretold of a good year ahead. The goats gave birth, Moza made delicious buttermilk and other Bedouin brought their needs. But as time slipped by, news of changes on the sand island reached their desert campsite.

"They have found black water called oil, there are buildings even bigger than the sheikh's fort and there are cars that can outrun any camel," a passing trader told them.

Abdullah listened carefully, but neither he nor Moza wished to make the journey.

"We are happy here, but if you boys wish to go, you have my blessing," he told his sons and saddling Rashid next morning, he and Moza watched them ride east in the direction of the coast.

Thus, life continued until the day Bilal brought a radio back from a visit to the island and a new ruler came on air to announce the death of the old sheikh.

"Your life is hard," he told the desert dwellers. "Come to the coast and share in our new oil wealth."

"I am missing our sons," Abdullah told Moza. And so, taking Jamila, he set off for the sea.

Now, however, instead of wading over to the island, he was able to cross on a bridge, beyond which stretched a black ribbon road.

"Aiee!" cried Abdullah. And worried the tarmac might hurt Jamila's feet, he continued walking along the edge, in the sand.

Soon he saw the changes for himself. High-rise buildings now dwarfed the fishermen's huts. There was a mosque and a dhow harbour and the well had become a fountain spraying water.

All that morning he wandered the streets inquiring if anyone knew of Sultan and Sayed. But the people were Indians and they could not understand what the old Arab was saying.

About to give up his search, Abdullah stopped outside a showroom filled with cars. BIN MOOSA: MERCEDES, BMW read a sign and peering through the window Abdullah recognised his eldest son.

He tapped on the glass with his camel stick. "Son! Son!"

"Father! Come in!" shouted Sultan jumping up from a desk.

"What has happened to our island? Who are these strangers? And where is your brother Sayed?" cried Abdullah all in one breath.

"*Alan bik!* A thousand welcomes!" said Sultan embracing him.

"Sayed is in Germany signing a deal," he explained. "How is mother? How many goats have we now?"

"There are many changes," he continued. "Instead of keeping money under the carpet, we put it in a bank. The men you see are Indian workers for the oil company."

Abdullah's sons had grown rich as the first licensed agency importing household goods, as well as expensive cars.

"Everyone drives," Sultan explained. "You must come here and live. There are free houses where you can turn on a tap instead of drawing well water."

"Lunchtime," he announced checking his watch.

Abdullah felt confused. Moza had only ever cooked when they were hungry, but he followed his son upstairs to an apartment above the showroom.

The door was opened by a servant and there was a table laden with food—mutton kebabs and fish curry, Kentucky Fried Chicken and chips served on bone china plates.

Accustomed to eating seated on the carpet in their tent, Abdullah found it hard to use a knife and fork while balancing on a chair.

"Use your fingers father," said Sultan, getting up to switch on a television.

The pictures of ships bigger than any dhow fascinated Abdullah. He saw trains and planes and things he'd never dreamt of. Then the program changed to an imam reciting from the Qur'an and with a jolt Abdullah realised he had not said his prayers that day.

It was the first time he'd ever forgotten and suddenly he felt uncomfortable in the glass and concrete environment.

Unable to sleep, he tossed and turned in a bedroom next to Sultan. He was missing Moza and the simple pleasure of smoking a *nargila* with Bilal. Come dawn, he crept downstairs to the still silent streets and found his way back to the fountain.

"*Yallah!* Let's go," he told Jamila. Then, turning for a last look at the island metropolis, they began the journey back to his familiar desert home.

~~~

ACKNOWLEDGEMENTS

The author would like to thank Carolynne Skinner of Parhelion Press for her valuable suggestions in the production of this book.

PICTURE CREDITS

Page 28   Falcons in Doha *souq* photograph Jill Brown/COPIX.
Page 51   Carpet shop photograph Anne Cook/COPIX.
Page 52   *Nargila* water pipe courtesy of the Amsterdam Pipe Museum, Prinsengracht 488, 1017 KH Amsterdam, NL.

All other photographs by the author.